ENGLISH

TEN STEPS
to improve your child's
READING
for ages 8–9

Let's learn at home

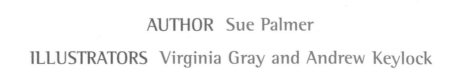

AUTHOR Sue Palmer

ILLUSTRATORS Virginia Gray and Andrew Keylock

Step
1

Think about what you read

Reading is about understanding. If you're not sure what a word or expression means, ask a grown-up or check in a dictionary.

Read this story and then answer the questions on pages 6 and 7.
▼

Say the names in this story like this: E-ko, Nar-sis-uss.

Echo and Narcissus

"Oh no, Echo's coming! Quick, let's get out of here!" The two nymphs hurried away down the mountain path. Echo was just in time to hear their giggles as they disappeared behind some rocks. This sort of thing happened quite often these days – Echo really couldn't understand it...

It wasn't that the others didn't like Echo – she was a sweet, kind nymph and very beautiful. It was just that she **talked** such a lot. And once she started talking, Echo couldn't seem to stop. It was like a vast, rolling river of talk. She chattered and nattered and clattered, on and on and on, about this and that and the other, until you wanted to scream. No one else could get a word in edgeways.

The only person in Greece who didn't find Echo's conversation boring was her boyfriend, Narcissus – and that was only because he was so interested in himself that he didn't actually notice anyone else! Every afternoon, Echo would talk to him for hours by the lakeside as he admired his reflection in the water, and he would nod happily, not even noticing her gossip. They suited each other very well! But in the mornings Narcissus liked to be alone. That was the dangerous time on the mountain – when Echo went out looking for other companions. The nymphs had learned to make their escape **before** she buttonholed them.

This particular morning, however, Echo spotted someone else to talk to. Walking along the mountain path a little ahead of her was a very tall, grand lady, with a richly embroidered cloak, and jewels woven into her hair. Most people would think twice before approaching such a splendid person, but Echo wasn't put off – she quickened her pace to catch up with her. Soon she had fallen into step beside the lady, and started what she thought was a very interesting conversation.

The lady glanced at her haughtily and walked a little faster – Echo walked a little faster too, and continued to chatter. The lady stopped and glared at Echo – a long, cold glare which would have frozen the blood of most nymphs. But Echo just carried on – she had gossiped through many glares in her time!

If Echo had known the stately lady's name, she might have thought twice. Hera, queen of the gods, was famous for her impatience and quick temper. Out for a brisk walk after an argument with her husband, Zeus, the last thing she wanted was this silly little chatterbox wittering away beside her. It wasn't long before she boiled over.

"Silence!" she cried, and the air around them vibrated with the power of her voice. Even Echo was silenced.

"Foolish nymph!" Hera's voice rang out. "You have chattered your last. From now on, the only words you will utter will be the words of others!"

"Words of others..." uttered Echo in surprise.

"Yes. You will spend your life repeating people's last words."

"Last words…" repeated Echo helplessly.

"And I hope it makes you very sorry!"

"Very sorry," gasped Echo in horror. And she fled, silent and tearful, down the mountain path.

Narcissus had just finished his bath, and was by the lake, posing and admiring his reflection in the water. He didn't even notice the desperate nymph, tears streaming down her cheeks, as she flung herself down beside him.

Echo tried to tell Narcissus what had happened, but her tongue was frozen in her mouth. She sat staring at him with hopeless eyes, gasping wordlessly. At last he saw her.

"What's the matter with you?" he asked.

"You!" echoed Echo, and her eyes widened in alarm as she realised what she'd said.

Narcissus was startled. "Me? What do you mean? Are you suggesting I'm not perfect?"

"Not perfect!" repeated Echo.

Narcissus snorted. He expected Echo to gaze at him adoringly, but she didn't look adoring today. In fact, she looked awful, with her tear-stained face, and her mouth opening and shutting like a fish. And she had insulted him – no one had ever suggested he wasn't perfect before, and Narcissus wasn't quite sure what to do.

"You stupid nymph!" he cried at last. "Of course, I'm perfect. You're lucky to have me as a boyfriend – you could be stuck with some vile, ugly man!"

"Vile, ugly man!" Echo yelled back, then clasped her hand over her mouth.

Narcissus flinched as though she had hit him. "Say you didn't mean that!" he shouted. "Say you didn't mean it this minute or find yourself another boyfriend."

"Another boyfriend," moaned Echo in despair.

Narcissus turned away from her. He was very shaken. He stared into the lake to make sure he was as handsome as ever. "Get out of my life," he muttered. "I never want to see you again. Now go!"

"Go!" repeated Echo, hopelessly. Then she turned and ran silently up the mountain path.

Up, up, she ran, to the highest peak, to throw herself on the ground and weep till she could weep no more. At last she fell into a painful sleep, and Zeus, who had been watching from the clouds, took pity on her. He pointed his mighty finger at the sleeping nymph and there was a roll of thunder. At once, her poor, sad body faded away, and nothing was left but an echoing memory.

Down by the lakeside, Narcissus sat staring at his reflection. Once Echo had gone, he never left the water's edge again – he just stared at himself, needing to know that he was perfect and beautiful. At last, he faded away too, and all that was left was another memory – a pale yellow flower nodding at its own image in the water.

And the memories are still there today – the echo chattering away in the mountains and the narcissus nodding to itself by the lake. They are all that is left of a beautiful nymph with too much conversation, and a handsome young man with too much pride.

1. In stories from Ancient Greece a nymph is:

someone who talks too much ☐

a goddess of nature, such as the rivers, the wood and mountains ☐

the queen of the gods ☐

Look back to the story if you want to check anything. You don't have to answer the questions from memory!

2. Why did the two nymphs hurry away from Echo?

. . . .

3. In what way did Echo and Narcissus 'suit each other very well'?

. . . .

. . . .

. . . .

4. Who was the 'very tall, grand lady' Echo saw on the mountain path?

. . . .

5. The phrase 'very tall, grand lady' tells us a little about what this character is like. Write down **six** more words and phrases which tell you about her character.

. . . .

. . . .

. . . .

6. How does Hera punish Echo for boring people with her endless gossip?

. . . .

7. Why does Narcissus like to sit by the lakeside?

. . . .

. . . .

8. Echo's first word to Narcissus is "You!"
   a) Why does she say this?

. . . .

. . . .

   b) What does Narcissus think she means?

. . . .

. . . .

9. Which three words describe Narcissus?

vain ☐   witty ☐   deceitful ☐

conceited ☐   humble ☐   self-centred ☐

What do the remaining three words mean? (Use a dictionary.)

. . . .

. . . .

. . . .

10. Who is Zeus? . . . .

How do you know from the story whether he is a god or a human being?

. . . .

. . . .

Dear Parent or Carer

Comprehension questions help children think about and understand what they read. If your child is unsure of the meaning of individual words, help him or her to look them up in a dictionary (see Step 2). Answers on pages 30 and 31.

When you finish this step put a sticker here!

Use your imagination

Writers sometimes use words in unusual ways to 'paint a picture' for the reader. You can use your imagination to work out when words have a **figurative** meaning.

> Words have straightforward meanings.

literal meaning

figurative meaning

> Words can also be used in special ways to compare one thing with another.

Here is some figurative language from *Echo and Narcissus*. Each time, say what the writer meant. The first one is done for you.

▼

It was like a vast, rolling river of talk.

Literal meaning	Figurative meaning
	Echo's talk was like a river because it rushed on and on and never stopped. It was a river gurgling and babbling.

It wasn't long before she boiled over.

Literal meaning	Figurative meaning
	. . . .
	. . . .
	. . . .
	. . . .

...her tongue was frozen in her mouth.

Literal meaning	Figurative meaning
	. . . .

The nymphs had learned to make their escape **before** she buttonholed them.

Literal meaning	Figurative meaning
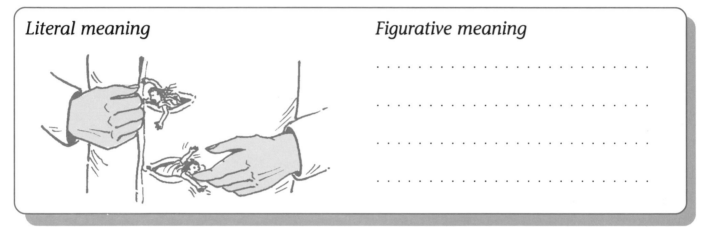	. . . .

Figures of speech

People often use figurative language without realising it. These expressions are called **figures of speech**. Guess these from the pictures and meanings.

▼

very happy indeed

talking nonsense

dreadful weather

. . . .

When you finish this step put a sticker here!

Dear Parent or Carer

This step helps your child to see the difference between literal and figurative uses of language. This is important for children's understanding of what they read and hear. Talk to your child about:
• interesting figures of speech that crop up in everyday conversation;
• imaginative language in books you read.
Discuss why it is effective – or why not. Answers on page 31.

Make your own fiction book

In the middle of this book there is a book cover for you to use to make your own story book called *Echo Mountain*.

Match the types of fiction to the descriptions.
The first one has been done for you.
▼

made-up stories set in the past, about real or invented characters in a real historical background

funny stories, which can be about real or fantasy people or creatures

stories about people, creatures or places that come from the author's imagination and do not exist in real life at all

stories made up by people long ago, about gods or heroes

stories of the future, space travel or things which have not yet been invented

stories in which animals are the main characters – often they behave as if they were people

stories about excitement, bravery and danger

There are lots of types of fiction. What sort will your *Echo Mountain* story be?

science fiction

myth or legend

humour

historical fiction

adventure

animal stories

fantasy

Plan your story

Think about your story before you start to write.

Middle?
(First event; development.)

Beginning?
(Opening line; setting the scene.)

End?
(Pulling it together; good last line.)

Characters?
(Names; personalities.)

Write your story

• Use A4 paper folded in half. Each sheet gives you four small pages, so work out how many pages you'll need before you start.

• Write your story, drawing illustrations to break it up (you could do these on small pieces of paper and stick them in).

• Draw a circle the same size as the one on the cover, draw a picture in it, cut it out and stick it on the cover.

• Add your name to the front cover (write it with a marker pen).

• Sew your book together.

When you finish this step put a sticker here!

Dear Parent or Carer

This step gives your child a chance to think about how a story book is put together. Help him or her to choose a particular type of story, and plan and write a 'first novel'. Who knows where it will lead! Answers on page 31.

Read different formats

The format of a piece of writing is the way it's set out on the page. Non-fiction comes in all sorts of formats.

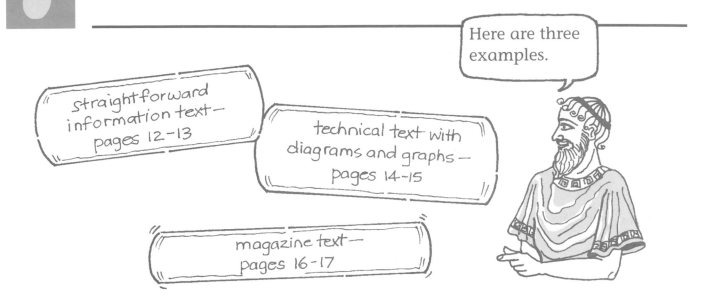

Here are three examples.

straightforward information text— pages 12–13

technical text with diagrams and graphs — pages 14–15

magazine text— pages 16–17

As you read, notice the difference in the way the pages are laid out.

▼

Bouncing Sounds

Introduction

Echoes are useful in many ways, both to humans and animals. Doctors use them to find out what is going on inside people's bodies; sailors and scientists use them to find out what is going on underwater; and some animals use them to find their way around. To understand how this works, you have to know what echoes are and why they happen.

What is an echo?

An echo is the reflection of a sound. When a sound hits something, it bounces back. If you stand 10 metres away from a very big wall and clap your hands, you should hear two sounds, one after the other. The first sound that reaches your ears is the sound of the clap. The second sound is the echo of the clap, bouncing back off the wall. The sound of the echo is softer and takes slightly longer to reach your ears than the clap itself.

Why do echoes happen?

Sound is caused by **vibration**. This could be the vibrations in someone's windpipe when they talk, or the vibrations that happen when two heavy objects hit each other. Every sound has vibrations as its starting point. The vibrations move outwards in waves from the starting point.

Sound waves can travel through air and water. They can even travel through solid things like iron, wood or the ground. They travel out in all directions from the starting point – just like ripples in a pond. If a sound wave reaches your ear, you hear the sound.

Sound waves travel outwards from the starting point like the ripples when you throw a pebble into a pond.

Sometimes a sound wave travelling through air or water hits something solid, so that some of the wave bounces back and starts to travel in the opposite direction. If this reflected sound wave reaches your ear, you hear an echo.

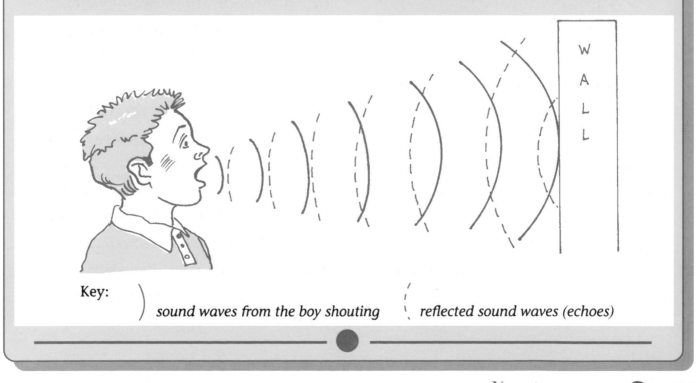

Key:

) *sound waves from the boy shouting*   \ *reflected sound waves (echoes)*

Now turn over

ECHOES AT SEA

The speed of sound

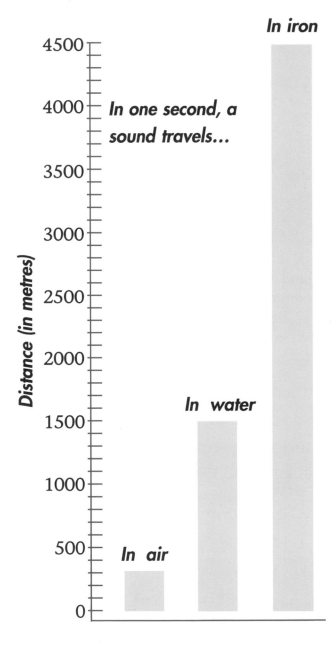

In iron

In one second, a sound travels...

In water

In air

Distance (in metres)

4500
4000
3500
3000
2500
2000
1500
1000
500
0

What is sonar?

Sonar is an invention that uses echoes to find out where things are underwater. People can use it to find out how far away things are, which way they are going and how fast they are moving. Sonar can also produce pictures of these things.

Sonar works best underwater because sound travels much further and faster in water than in air. A loud sound that takes five seconds to reach you through air would take little more than one second to reach you if you were underwater. This is because particles of water are closer to each other than particles of air, so the sound waves travel through them more easily.

How sonar works

There are two parts to an underwater sonar device – a **transmitter** and a

---

Sonar is used:
- **by the navy to find ships, submarines and underwater mines**
- **by scientists to look at the bottoms of oceans and lakes, so they** **can use computers to make maps of the land under the water**
- **by fishermen, on big fishing trips, to find the biggest catches of fish.**

receiver. The **transmitter** sends a sharp 'pinging' sound underneath the ship. The sound waves travel through the water until they hit something in the sea – or the bottom of the ocean. Let's say they hit a shoal of fish.

The sound waves bounce off the shoal of fish, and send an echo back through the water. The **receiver** on the ship picks up the echo and turns it into electrical signals, which you can see on a screen. The sailors look at the screen and see how far away the shoal of fish is, and how big it is.

S
O U N D
N A V I G A T I O N
– finding your way around.
A N D
R A N G I N G
– judging distances.

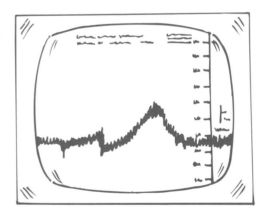

A sonar screen

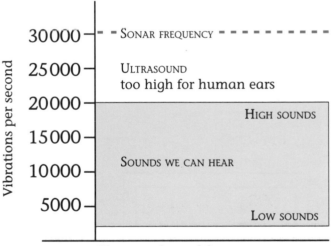

The sounds used for sonar are too high for human beings to hear.

Sound always travels through water at the same speed – 1500 metres a second.

So you can work out how far away something is by measuring the length of time it takes for the receiver to pick up the echo. (You have to divide the distance by two, because the sound waves have to travel there and back.)

Echoes in the body

Sometimes doctors need to look inside people's bodies to see what's going on. Usually they just take an X-ray, but in some circumstances X-rays can be dangerous, and they need another method of seeing through someone's skin. So scientists invented a way of using echoes to look inside the human body. It is called ultrasound.

The ultrasound machine sends a very high-pitched sound (so high that we cannot hear it at all) into the body. The sound bounces off the flesh and muscles inside the body, and echoes come back to the machine. The echoes make patterns and a computer turns them into a photograph – or moving picture on a television screen.

Doctors use ultrasound to help people with lots of different sorts of illnesses. One of them is heart disease. Ultrasound lets doctors study the hearts of people with heart disease to find out what is wrong, so they can perhaps find a cure.

Doctors also often use ultrasound to look at unborn babies. An unborn baby growing inside its mother's womb is called a foetus. A foetus could be damaged by X-rays, so doctors use ultrasound to look at it instead. They can use ultrasound to keep track of how the foetus is growing, and to make sure it is well. They can check when

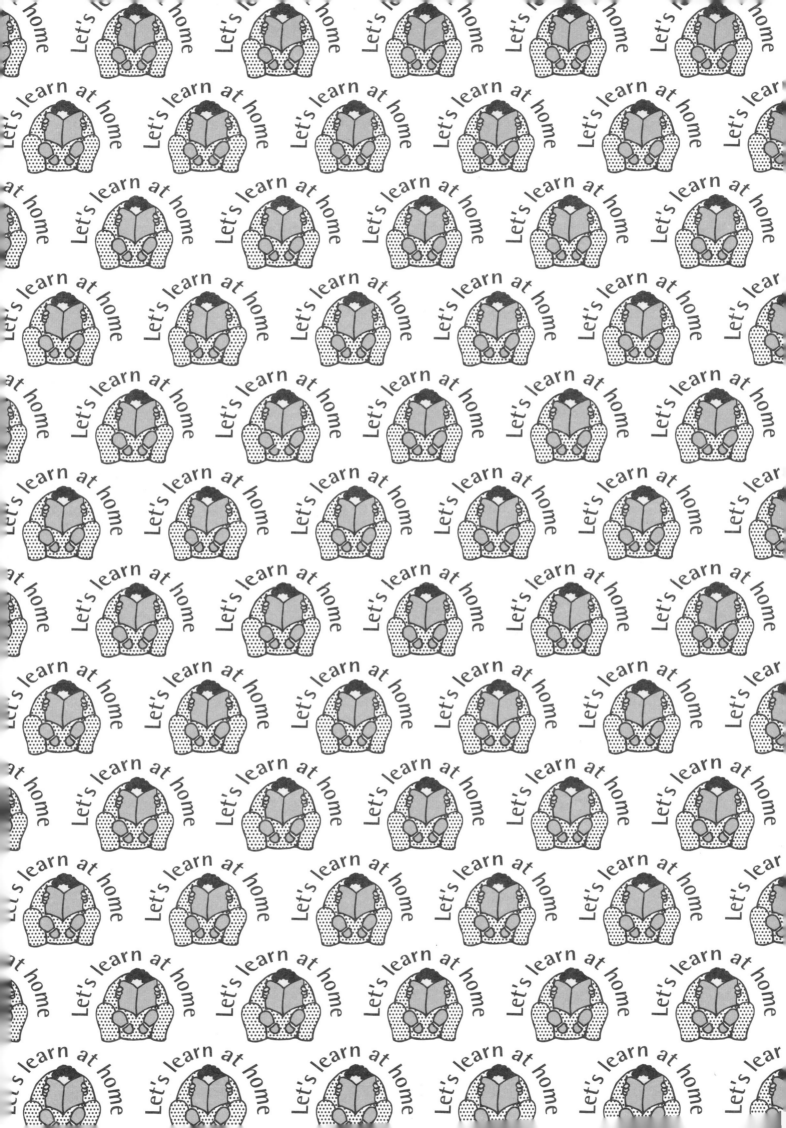

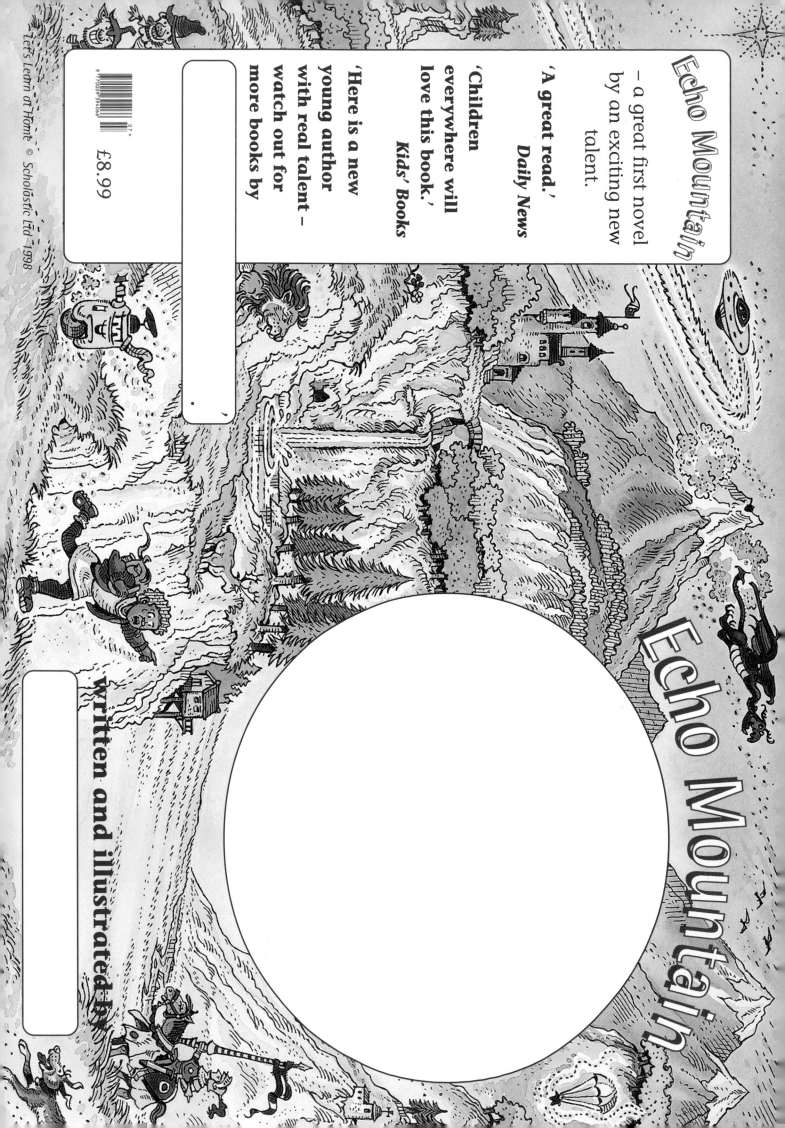

Echo Mountain

– a great first novel by an exciting new talent.

'A great read.'
Daily News

'Children everywhere will love this book.'
Kids' Books

'Here is a new young author with real talent – watch out for more books by

written and illustrated by

Echo Mountain

£8.99

9 770009 394066   07>

Bats and Echoes

- How do bats find their way about in the dark?

- What do bats have in common with fishermen and underwater scientists?

- How can you 'see' through sound?

This fascinating book answers all these questions – and more – about one of the greatest miracles of nature.

by

£8.99

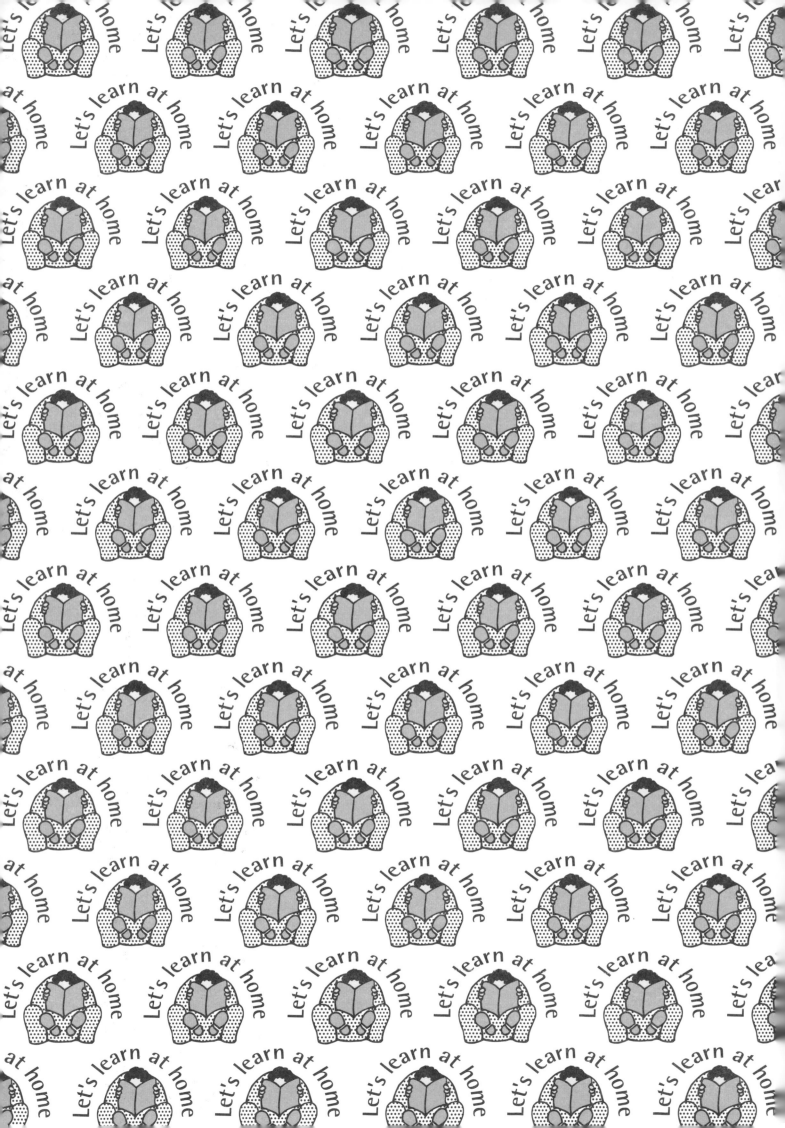

A doctor using ultrasound on a pregnant woman. You can see the transducer being held by the doctor on the woman's stomach, and the pictures of the foetus will appear on the TV screens around them.

the baby is due to be born by measuring the size of its head. Most pregnant women now have at least one ultrasound check.

The part of the ultrasound machine that sends out the sounds and receives the echoes is called a **transducer**. The doctor spreads a sort of jelly on the skin of the mother's stomach, then presses the transducer against it. The jelly helps the high-pitched sounds travel more easily into the mother's body.

The mother can then see a fuzzy picture of the foetus inside her on the television screen. Sometimes she gets a photograph to take home, too.

Which format do you like most?

information ✓ technical ☐ magazine ☐

From which section did you learn most?

information ☐ technical ☐ magazine ☐

When you finish this step put a sticker here!

Read to learn

When you know your way round a variety of non-fiction texts, you can find out the answers to all sorts of questions.

Look back to pages 12–17 to answer these questions.
You don't have to do them from memory.

▼

1. What is an echo?

. . . .

. . . .

2. Name three things that sound waves can travel through.

. . . .

. . . .

3. How did sonar get its name?

. . . .

. . . .

. . . .

4. List three purposes for which sonar is used.

. . . .

. . . .

. . . .

twice as fast ☐

5. Sound travels through iron 3 times slower ☐ than it travels through water.

15 times slower ☐

3 times faster ☐

18

6. Write the labels for these diagrams to explain what is happening.

7. In what way is an ultrasound machine like an X-ray machine?

. . . .

8. What is the highest frequency of sound vibration that most human beings can hear?

. . . .

9. What is a **transducer**?

. . . .

. . . .

10. What is the **title** of the technical pages (pages 14–15)?

. . . .

Think of another title that would cover everything on those pages.

. . . .

Let punctuation guide you

Punctuation marks show you the tone of voice you should use to read, and where to change it, as well as where you should pause to break the text into meaningful chunks.

> Everyone knows that we're the three marks that can finish a sentence, but do you know the ones that work inside a sentence?

dash –

brackets ( )

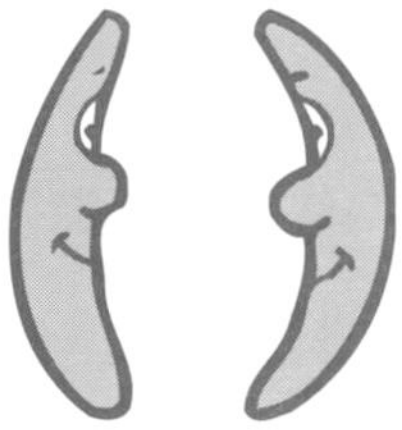

hyphen -

"inverted commas"

comma,

three dots ...

Match the punctuation marks to the descriptions.
▼

These are put round a group of words to separate them off from the rest of the sentence. The words are spoken 'on the side'.

These can show:
- that someone is speaking
- that a word is spoken in a special tone because it is being used in a unusual way.

This shows a slight pause inside a sentence.

These show that a sentence trails off, or that words are missing.

This shows a sharp break inside a sentence (longer than a comma).

This punctuation mark sticks bits of words together.

Use a coloured pen to go over all the punctuation marks in these extracts.
Then read them aloud, paying special attention to the punctuation. Let it help you make the meaning clear.

▼

"Oh no, Echo's coming! Quick, let's get out of here!" The two nymphs hurried away down the mountain path. Echo was just in time to hear their giggles as they disappeared behind some rocks. This sort of thing happened quite often these days – Echo really couldn't understand it…

Down by the lakeside, Narcissus sat staring at his reflection. Once Echo had gone, he never left the water's edge again – he just stared at himself, needing to know that he was perfect and beautiful.

Sound waves can travel through air and water. They can even travel through solid things like iron, wood or the ground. They travel out in all directions from the starting point – just like ripples in a pond.

The ultrasound machine sends a very high-pitched sound (so high that we cannot hear it at all) into the body.

When you finish this step put a sticker here!

Try reading into a tape recorder and listening to yourself. Can you tell where punctuation marks come by listening to your voice?

Dear Parent or Carer
This step shows your child that punctuation is meant as a guide to the reader. Attending to punctuation can improve your child's expression when reading aloud. It can also help him or her make sense of sentences when reading silently. Answers on page 32.

Use your library

If you know how to find books at your library, you can look up anything you need to know.

Each subject has a number. All the books on that subject will be together on the shelf.

Non-fiction books in a library are kept together in subject groups.

You can find the number of the subject from the library index.

Dewey numbers

Many libraries number their books using Dewey numbers (Dewey decimal classification). They start at 0 and go up to 1000. This is how the subjects are split up.

000 Sources of information
For example, computers, newspapers.

100 Philosophy and psychology
For example, beliefs of ancient times, how people think.

200 Religion
For example, Christianity, Islam.

300 Social sciences
For example, transport, fashion, customs, folklore.

400 Languages
For example, English, French, Urdu.

500 Natural sciences and maths
For example, the earth, animals, space, numbers.

600 Technology
For example, engineering, medicine, farming, pets, cooking, buildings.

700 The arts and hobbies
For example, painting, music, dance, theatre, sport.

800 Literature
For example, poetry, plays.

900 Geography and history
For example, places, famous people, world history.

If you are studying a topic, you need to know where to look for books. Write down the nearest 'hundred' in the Dewey system for these topics.

▼

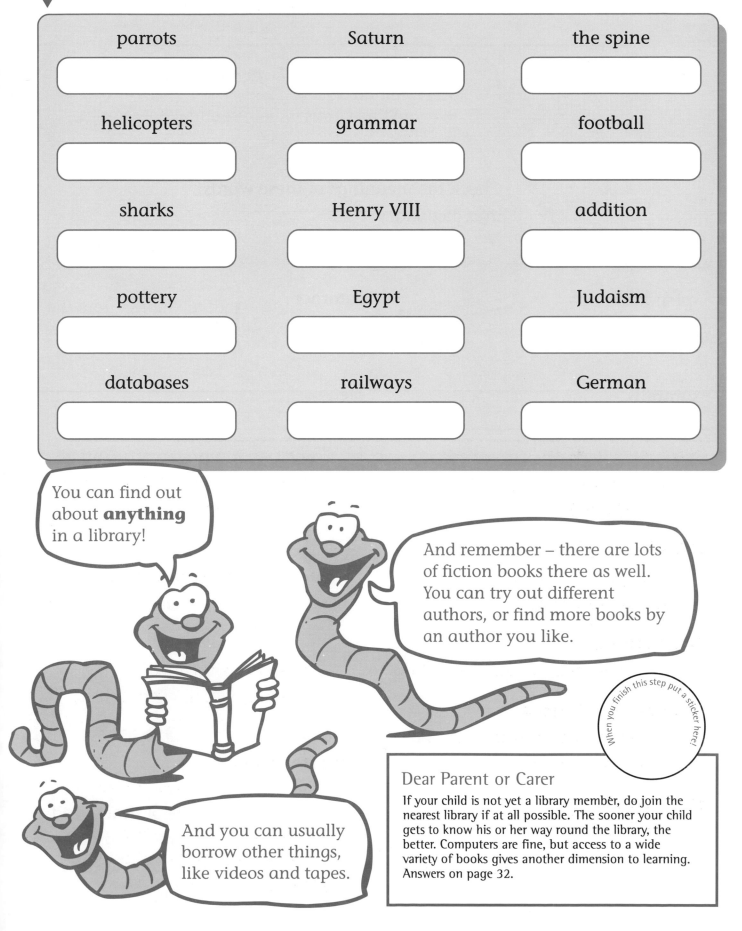

parrots

Saturn

the spine

helicopters

grammar

football

sharks

Henry VIII

addition

pottery

Egypt

Judaism

databases

railways

German

You can find out about **anything** in a library!

And remember – there are lots of fiction books there as well. You can try out different authors, or find more books by an author you like.

When you finish this step put a sticker here!

And you can usually borrow other things, like videos and tapes.

Dear Parent or Carer

If your child is not yet a library member, do join the nearest library if at all possible. The sooner your child gets to know his or her way round the library, the better. Computers are fine, but access to a wide variety of books gives another dimension to learning. Answers on page 32.

Make sense of poetry

Some poems look a bit difficult, but if you take time to make sense of them, they can be very beautiful.

1
Make sure you know the literal meaning of all the words.

The poem on page 25 is about echoes. It was written over a hundred years ago.
Here are three hints to help you make sense of it.

Check the meanings of these words in a dictionary.
▼

splendour . . . .   cataract . . . .

. . . .

summits . . . .   glens . . . .

. . . .

2
Remember that poets often use figurative language.

What do you think the poet might mean by these lines?
▼

The long light shakes across the lakes

. . . .

The horns of Elfland

. . . .

3
Punctuation is very important in poetry. Let it guide you in the way you read it.

Read the poem in your head a couple of times, and try to work out what it means. Then read it aloud – enjoy the rhyme and rhythm, and try to make the poem come alive through your reading.   ▶

The splendour falls on castle walls
And snowy summits old in story –
The long light shakes across the lakes
And the wild cataract leaps in glory.
Blow, bugle, blow, set the wild echoes flying!
Blow, bugle – answer, echoes,
        dying… dying… dying.

O hark, O hear! how thin and clear,
And thinner, clearer, farther going!
O sweet and far from cliff and scar
The horns of Elfland faintly blowing!
Blow, let us hear the purple glens replying –
Blow, bugle – answer, echoes,
        dying… dying… dying.

Alfred, Lord Tennyson (1809–1892)

When you finish this step put a sticker here!

Dear Parent or Carer
Ask your child to practise this poem, using the hints on the opposite page. Then let him or her give you a special performance. How effective is the reading? Answers on page 32.

Make a non-fiction book

In the middle of this book there is a book cover for you to use to make your own non-fiction book called *Bats and Echoes*.

Have you ever heard people say 'blind as a bat'? Well, we aren't blind – but we can't rely on our eyes because we fly around in the pitch dark.

We find our way by making high-pitched squeaks and listening for echoes – just like sonar. If you've done Steps 4 and 5, you can imagine how it works.

Lots of people don't know how bats use echoes. Write a little book to explain it to them. Make notes so you can write four sections with these headings. Some have been done for you.

▼

What is an echo? (See page 12.)

. . . .

. . . .

. . . .

. . . .

What is sonar? (See page 14.)

. . . .

. . . .

. . . .

. . . .

Why do bats need 'sonar'?

'Blind as a bat' not true. Can see a bit. Mostly on move in dark.

How to find prey? How to avoid bumping into things?

How do bats use echoes?

Night – bats fly about – make high-pitched sounds (ultrasound).

Sounds bounce off things (echoes) – back to bat – brain like computer.

If prey – swoop.

If obstruction – avoid.

Cut this page out and use these pictures to illustrate your book. Before you cut them out, read the instructions on the other side of the page (page 28).

Dear Parent or Carer
This step helps your child think about how a non-fiction book is put together. It needs careful planning and attention to the instructions on these pages. Encourage your child to make notes, using pages 12–17. If possible, look in other books for further information.

When you finish this step put a sticker here!

• Use A4 paper folded in half. Each sheet gives you four small pages – so work out how many pages you'll need before you start.

• Leave the first page blank. At the end, you can turn it into a contents page.

• Space out your work – don't let it get too crushed up.

• Cut out the illustrations and use them to break up and help explain the text.
  – Give pictures captions.
  – Write labels for diagrams.
  – Add more illustrations if you like.

• You could add an index or a glossary at the back, if there's room.

• Write your name on the front cover, using a marker pen.

• Sew your book together.

Read, read, read!

The more you read, the easier you'll find it. The more you **think about** what you read, the better you'll be at reading.

What makes a good book? Think about books you've enjoyed, and books you've learned from.

My top ten good books:
▼

	Title	Author	Why I liked it
1	. . . .	. . . .	. . . .
2	. . . .	. . . .	. . . .
3	. . . .	. . . .	. . . .
4	. . . .	. . . .	. . . .
5	. . . .	. . . .	. . . .
6	. . . .	. . . .	. . . .
7	. . . .	. . . .	. . . .
8	. . . .	. . . .	. . . .
9	. . . .	. . . .	. . . .
10	. . . .	. . . .	. . . .

When you finish this step put a sticker here!

Good luck finding more good books! And good reading!

Dear Parent or Carer

Help your child find more good books by taking him or her to the library, giving books, audiobooks and book tokens as presents and reading bedtime stories. Your child will be encouraged to become a more critical reader if you talk to each other about books you share.

Parents' pages

Reading is probably the most important skill your child will ever learn. It is the passport to success in the educational system, to endless personal pleasure and to all the knowledge contained in the libraries of the world.

The coming of the computer age does not lessen the importance of reading – indeed, using a computer depends on reading skills. The more information available to us through the mass media and the Internet, the more important fluent, critical reading becomes.

Encouragement at home in the early stages is one of the most important factors in developing children's reading skills.

Reading skills

Reading involves a mixture of skills. By the age of 7, most children recognise common words on sight. They work out unknown words by a mixture of:

- working out their sounds;
- blending sounds together;
- guessing possible meanings.

If your child has trouble with an unknown word, help by giving clues based on one or more of the above.

Reading comprehension

Reading is about understanding – of words, phrases, sentences and whole texts. Readers need a wide range of understanding to:

- answer straightforward questions;
- read between the lines;
- appreciate the way something is expressed;
- read critically, looking for evidence.

Steps 1, 2, 4 and 8 give opportunities to develop all these types of reading.

Help your child think about what he or she reads by talking about the books you share.

Reasons for reading

We read in different ways depending on what and why we are reading. Awareness of the different types of reading helps children become more efficient. The differences also affect the way different texts are written, illustrated and set out on the page. Steps 3 and 9 help your child look closely at the way fiction and non-fiction books are structured, and Step 4 features three common types of non-fiction text.

Help your child notice the wide variety of texts you read at home – particularly non-fiction texts such as recipes, catalogues and reference books. Talk about the significant ways in which they differ, and how best to read them.

Wider reading

Once skills are established, the way for children to become better readers is by reading. Steps 7 and 10 encourage wider reading, but your child also needs your interest, encouragement and example.

Remember that reading doesn't just mean stories. Comics, magazines, CD-ROMs, poems, non-fiction books and reference books can all be valuable reading material. Work from your child's interests – once he or she has reading skills that are well-established you can help widen the range and increase the challenge.

 Step 1 Think about what you read

Pages 6–7: 1. a goddess of nature, such as the rivers, the wood and mountains
Accept any reasonable answer based on the text for the following questions, for example:
2. to escape from Echo before she could start talking to them (they thought she talked far too much)

3. Narcissus suited Echo because he was good-looking and too absorbed in himself to notice how boring she could be; Echo suited Narcissus because she gazed at him adoringly and didn't notice he wasn't listening to her.
4. Hera (queen of the gods)
5. Any six of the following (or individual describing words from phrases) are correct: with a richly embroidered cloak, and jewels woven into her hair; a splendid person; haughtily; glared; a long, cold glare which would have frozen the blood of most nymphs; the stately lady's; famous for her impatience and quick temper; thinks of Echo as a 'silly little chatterbox wittering away beside her'; boiled over; the air around them vibrated with the power of her voice; calls Echo a 'Foolish nymph'
6. She takes away Echo's power of speech, leaving her only to repeat the last words spoken by other people, that is, as an 'echo'.
7. He likes to look at his reflection in the water (also, he bathes in it each morning).

from the author's imagination and do not exist in real life at all → fantasy
stories made up by people long ago, about gods or heroes → myth or legend
stories of the future, space travel or things which have not yet been invented → science fiction
stories in which animals are the main characters – often they behave as if they were people → animal stories
stories about excitement, bravery and danger → adventure

8. a) because she repeats the last word spoken to her by Narcissus
b) Narcissus thinks she is answering his question, 'What's the matter with you?' with the explanation that it is he himself who is at fault: 'You!'
9. vain, conceited, self-centred
witty – clever; amusing
deceitful – cheating; false
humble – having low self-importance
10. Hera's husband
He is a god – he watches from the clouds, causes thunder to roll and makes Echo fade away.

 Step 2 Use your imagination

Pages 8–9: Accept any answers similar to: Hera's anger was like water in a pan on the heat, bubbling up gradually, then coming out all at once; when something is frozen it cannot move – Echo was so upset, she couldn't speak; when you put a button in its buttonhole, you pin it down in the same place, not allowing it to escape – the nymphs knew that once Echo had stopped them they wouldn't be allowed to get away.

dreadful weather – raining cats and dogs
very happy indeed – over the moon
talking nonsense – talking through your hat

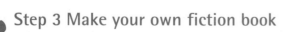 Step 3 Make your own fiction book

Page 10: funny stories, which can be about real or fantasy people or creatures → humour
stories about people, creatures or places that come

 Step 5 Read to learn

Pages 18–19: Accept any answers similar to:
1. the reflection of a sound; a bouncing sound; an echo occurs when sound waves travelling through air or water are reflected back off something solid
2. air, water, and solid objects (iron, wood and the ground, for example)
3. from the initial letters of these words: **s**ound (first two letters), **n**avigation **a**nd **r**anging
4. to find other ships, submarines and mines; for scientific investigation and underwater mapping; for fishing
5. Sound travels through iron **3 times faster** than it travels through water.

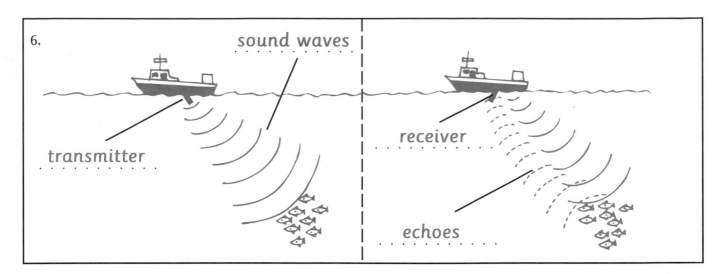

6.

sound waves

transmitter

receiver

echoes

7. It helps doctors see inside people's bodies.
8. 20000
9. the part of an ultrasound machine which sends out sound and receives echoes (transmitter/receiver)
10. Echoes at Sea
Children think of their own title – check that it covers the subject adequately, for example *Using Echoes*.

 Step 6 Let punctuation guide you

Page 20: dash → This shows a sharp break inside a sentence (longer than a comma).
brackets → These are put round a group of words to separate them off from the rest of the sentence. The words are spoken 'on the side'.
hyphen → This punctuation mark sticks bits of words together.
inverted commas → These can show:
• that someone is speaking
• that a word is spoken in a special tone because it is being used in an unusual way.
comma → This shows a slight pause inside a sentence.
three dots → These show that a sentence trails off, or that words are missing.

 Step 7 Use your library

Pages 22–23: (Across from left to right)
parrots – 500/600; Saturn – 500; the spine 500/600; helicopters – 300/600; grammar – 400; football – 700; sharks – 500; Henry VIII – 900; addition – 500; pottery – 700; Egypt – 900; Judaism – 200; databases – 000; railways – 300/600; German – 400.

Note: for some subjects there is more than one correct answer.

 Step 8 Make sense of poetry

Pages 24–25: splendour – glory, brightness
summits – the tops of mountains
cataract – a waterfall (also, a condition in which the lens of the eye becomes opaque and vision is blurred)
glens – valleys

The long light shakes across the lakes – light seeming to flicker on the water due to the waves
The horns of Elfland – thin echoes of the bugle, like fairy music